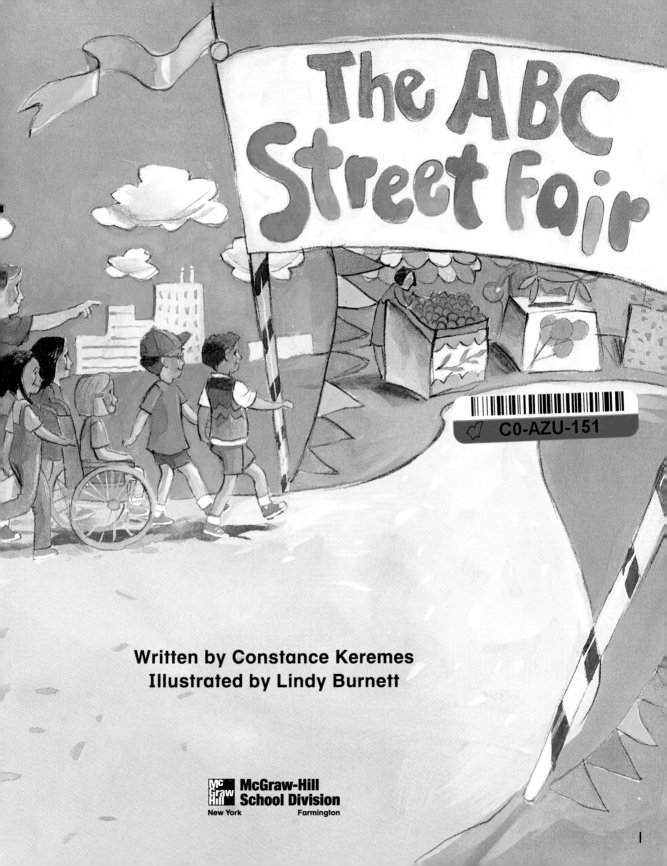

The ABC Street Fair

Written by Constance Keremes
Illustrated by Lindy Burnett

McGraw-Hill
School Division
New York   Farmington

Aa

Anna's **a**pples

Beautiful **b**alloons

Bb

Cc

Colorful costumes

Dd

Delicious **d**esserts

Eddie's **e**ggs

Ee

Funny faces

Gg

Good **g**ame

Happy **h**ippos

Ii

Interesting instruments

Jj

Jolly juggler

Keisha's **k**ites

Long line

Mm

Marvelous marbles

Nice **n**ecklaces

Nn

Oo

Odd **o**bjects

Panda **p**uppets

Qq

Quincy's **q**uilts

Red **r**oses

Rr

Ss

Super **s**andwiches

Tasty tacos

Uu

Unusual **u**mbrellas

Valuable **v**ases

Ww

Warm **w**affles

Six boxes

Yy

Yellow **y**o-yos

Zany **z**ebra